CRICKET Quiz Book

Marshall Cavendish London & New York

Picture Credits

Central Press 10, 13T, 15T, 16, 25T, 32R, 34BR, 38TR, 42R, 44L, 45R, 52T, 53BL, 59R, 74T

Colorsport 53TL, 59L, 63

Patrick Eagar 18B, 28C&B, 29, 32L, 34T, 34BL, 35, 41T&B, 42B, 50, 51T&B, 52BL, 54, 55, 56L, 57, 60TL&R, 61R, 62L&BR, 64, 67TL&BR, 74B, 79R&B, 80TR&BR, 84L&R, 91L&R

Fox Photos 20T&B, 26, 38TL

Ray Green 70T

ITN 71T

Indian Express Newspapers 79TL

Ken Kelly 5, 8T, 15B, 42T, 67L, 80L, 81

Keystone 8B, 38B, 42L

New Zealand High Commission 28T

Popperfoto 44TR, 88T

Press Association 20B, 21, 52BR, 58TR&BR, 61BL, 85

Rex Features 70B

Sport & General 60BL, 61TL, 62TR, 71B

Syndication International 44BR, 44L

UPI 9, 88B

Quiz compiled by Jonathan Culverhouse, of the Daily Mail

With thanks to the Walters brothers, Ken Willson and Barry Wright for their help with the questions and John Newth for checking the answers.

Picture research: Mark Dartford

Published by
Marshall Cavendish Books Limited
58 Old Compton Street
London W1V 5PA

This volume first published 1979

© Marshall Cavendish Limited 1979

Printed in Gt. Britain by C. J. Mason & Sons Ltd., Bristol,

ISBN 0 85685 713 0

Introduction

As well as testing your knowledge of cricket with dozens of picture questions, the Cricket Quizbook includes more than 500 other questions designed for you to play an entertaining 'match' against your friends and family, or on your own.

'Go for the Runs' is divided into three sections – quick singles, which are relatively easy, fours, which are more difficult, and sixes, which are quite tough.

Decide who's going to bat first, and fire away with the questions. The batsman, of course, can choose whether to go for a quick single, a four or a six, scoring the appropriate runs for a correct answer.

Don't be frightened to go for the odd four or six – you never know whether you'll be bowled what for you is a dolly-drop of a question.

But you're out of course if you're stumped on any of the questions.

After you've lost ten wickets, it's your opponent's turn to bat. You can try variations, like taking it in turn to bowl, having a limited number of 'overs' per side, or using a team of batsmen, depending on numbers.

Good luck!

To find the answers to the "Go For The Runs" questions –
take the number of the question in the top row of boxes and
then the number below it in the second row of boxes refers
to the answer number.

Unless otherwise stated, all questions refer
to first-class cricket.
* signifies 'not out'.

Contents

1. Identify this batsman.
2. In which year and against whom did he score
   two double Test centuries?
3. What was the record he set in that same year?

Go for the runs!

1. What nationality is Ken McEwan?
2. Under which name did England tour until 1977?
3. What was unique about Geoff Boycott's 100th first class century?
4. Which Australian started a pirate series in 1977?
5. What is Lancashire's emblem?
6. Who were the respective captains in the England-Australia Centenary Test?
7. Who was England's reserve wicket-keeper on the 1978/79 tour of Australia?
8. What was Frank Tyson's nickname?
9. Name the three Ws.
10. Who is the only bowler to have taken all ten wickets in a Test innings?

11. Which two batsmen figured in a last-wicket stand of 98 for Australia against England at Old Trafford in 1961?
12. Who scored his maiden Test century for England against the West Indies in 1976?
13. In which series did India first win a rubber against England?
14. Who was the first player to score a Test century?

15. Who was the last Englishman to take a Test hat-trick?

1	2	3	4	5	6	7	8	9	10	11	12	13	14	15
6	5	4	3	2	1	11	7	8	9	10	15	14	13	12

Answers: **1.** Tony Greig (England) and Greg Chappell **2.** A red rose **3.** Kerry Packer **4.** It's the only one to have been scored in a Test match **5.** M.C.C. **6.** South African **7.** Typhoon **8.** Sir Frank Worrell, Everton Weekes and Clyde Walcott **9.** Jim Laker **10.** Alan Davidson and Graham McKenzie **11.** Roger Tolchard (replaced by David Bairstow after injury) **12.** Peter Loader v West Indies, Headingley, 1957 **13.** Charles Bannerman for Australia v England, 1877 **14.** 1961/62 **15.** David Steele.

Go for the runs!

1. True or false: India last played South Africa in 1968.
2. Who is Australia's leading Test wicket-taker?
3. At which ground did Jim Laker take his record 19 wickets in a Test?
4. Whose Christian names are these: Denis Charles Scott?
5. Who was recalled as Australia's captain after Greg Chappell?
6. By what score did England win the 1978/79 Ashes series?
7. For which form of cricket was a yellow ball first used?
8. Which England bowler took four wickets in five balls during the first Test against Pakistan in 1978?
9. After how many six ball overs is the new ball due?
10. How often is the Prudential World Cup held?

11. Who were the beaten semi-finalists in the 1975 Prudential World Cup?
12. Whose record did Rodney Hogg break for most wickets by an Australian in an Ashes series?
13. Who was the last South African tour captain in England?
14. Who played for the Guinness Trophy?

15. Who is the only cricketer to have played for England and India?

1	2	3	4	5	6	7	8	9	10	11	12	13	14	15
9	8	7	6	5	4	3	2	1	15	14	13	12	11	10

Answers: **1.** 85 **2.** Chris Old **3.** A Kerry Packer floodlit game **4.** 5–1 **5.** Bobby Simpson **6.** Denis Compton **7.** Old Trafford, Manchester **8.** Richie Benaud, 248 **9.** False—India have never played South Africa **10.** The Nawab of Pataudi (senior) **11.** England and the Rest of the World, 1970 **12.** Peter van der Merwe **13.** Arthur Mailey **14.** England and New Zealand **15.** Every four years.

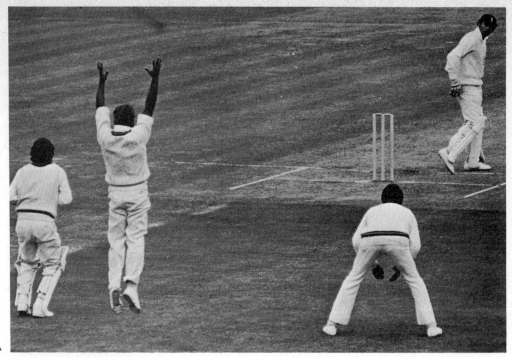

A

How's That?

A.
1. Who were the batsman and the first slip involved in this controversial incident at Edgbaston in 1973?
2. Who was the umpire involved?
3. What was the appeal and the verdict?
4. What happened as a result?

B
1. Who's the unlucky batsman?
2. Who were the opposition?
3. It was this batsman's last match as his country's captain—which and where was it?

B

C

1. Which two countries were contesting this match?
2. Who are the bowler, batsman and wicketkeeper?

C

Puzzle A

Don't let these post-War Test players stump you!

1. . . . . will repair your machine.
2. Rain could turn . . . . into a . . . .
3. It sounds as if . . . . could make you a coat.
4. But . . . . might tie you up.

Puzzle B

Find the England captain:

1. He's always near . . . .
2. He's no lady but follows one . . . .
3. But don't worry, he'll be there . . . .
4. He'll replace your horse's shoe . . . .

1. Where and in which Test series would you have seen this scene?
2. Who is reflecting on the state of the pitch?
3. What was the state of play when it was held up?
4. How did play eventually restart?
5. What was the nail-biting climax?
6. Which bowler proved the deciding factor and what were his innings figures?
7. How did the result affect the series and the Ashes?

Go for the runs!

Quick 1 Singles

1. Was the first Test series between New Zealand and Australia in 1925, 1935 or 1945?
2. What is a long hop?
3. Is Mick Malone an Australian fast bowler or spinner?
4. Which country won their first ever Test match in England in 1971?
5. Against whom did England play a Test series at home in 1970?
6. In which country would you be if you were watching a Currie Cup match?
7. Which Australian State side plays at Melbourne?
8. What colour caps do West Indian Test players wear?
9. How long is a standard cricket pitch?
10. Who was Australia's wicket-keeper for the 1978/79 Test series against England?

Score a 4

11. What was the unique result produced by the Brisbane Test between Australia and the West Indies in the 1960/61 series?
12. Off which bowler did Sir Gary Sobers hit his record-breaking 36 runs in an over in 1968?
13. What is the highest innings total England have made against Australia?
14. In which year did England last play a Test series against South Africa?

6 Hit

15. Which *two* players scored centuries in the Centenary Test between England and Australia in 1977?

1	2	3	4	5	6	7	8	9	10	11	12	13	14	15
8	9	10	11	12	13	14	15	7	6	5	4	2	1	3

Answers: **1.** 1965 **2.** 903–7 dec., Oval, 1938 **3.** Derek Randall (England, 174) and Rodney Marsh (Australia, 110 not out) **4.** Glamorgan's Malcolm Nash **5.** It's the only Test to be tied **6.** John McLean (replaced by Kevin Wright) **7.** 22 yards (20.1 m) **8.** 1945 **9.** A short-pitched ball **10.** Fast bowler **11.** India **12.** The Rest of the World **13.** South Africa or Rhodesia **14.** Victoria **15.** Maroon.

Go for the runs!

Quick Singles 1

1. Who holds the highest batting average for an English season?
2. Who won the 1975/76 West Indies v India series?
3. Who won the Prudential World Cup in 1975?
4. What were the Christian names of W. G. Grace?
5. What is the name of Cambridge University's ground?
6. Who was England's principal 'bodyline' bowler in the 1932/33 tour of Australia?
7. At which Test ground would you find the Kirkstall Lane end?
8. In which Test did Tony Greig make his debut as England captain?
9. Which English county plays at Taunton?
10. How can you be out from a no-ball?

Score a 4

11. Who is Australia's leading wicket-keeper and whose record did he take?
12. Who is England's leading Test run-maker?
13. Who holds the record for most Test stumpings?
14. Which Australian has taken most wickets in a Test innings?

6 Hit

15. Who was the last Englishman to score a century in each innings of a Test match?

1	2	3	4	5	6	7	8	9	10	11	12	13	14	15
11	10	9	8	7	15	14	12	13	6	5	4	1	2	3

Answers: **1.** W. A. Oldfield (Australia) 52 **2.** A. A. Mailey (Australia) 9–121 v England 1920/21 **3.** Denis Compton v Australia 1946/47 **4.** Colin Cowdrey, 7,624 **5.** Rodney Marsh (198 dismissals), Wally Grout (187) **6.** By a run-out, obstructing the field, handling the ball or hitting the ball twice **7.** Fenners **8.** William Gilbert **9.** West Indies **10.** West Indies **11.** Sir Don Bradman (115.66 in 1938) **12.** 2nd Test v Australia, 1975 **13.** Somerset **14.** Headingley, Leeds **15.** Harold Larwood.

4

1. Who is this batsman?
2. He set a record in 1938 which stood for 20 years—what was it and who broke it?
3. What was his first score in Test cricket?

5

1. Who is this batsman?
2. What is his highest Test score?
3. What record did he set as England captain?
4. What are his Christian names in full?

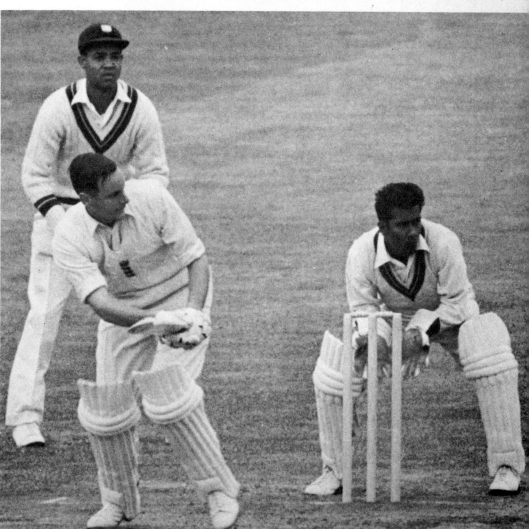

Go for the runs!

1. What is the maximum width of a cricket bat?
2. Which West Indian island plays at Sabina Park?
3. Between which two English universities is the Varsity match played?
4. Which wicket-keeper has made most Test dismissals?
5. After how many eight-ball overs is the new ball due?
6. On which ground was the Australia-England Centenary Test played?
7. Who captained New Zealand on the 1978 tour of England?
8. Who was controversially sacked as Yorkshire captain in 1978?
9. What is a 'chinaman'?
10. In which city would you find the Edgbaston ground?

11. On which ground in 1938 did Sir Len Hutton make his then record score of 364?
12. The Wisden Trophy is awarded to the winners of the Test series between which two countries?
13. What is Australia's highest Test score?
14. Who won the Man of the Match award in the 1975 Prudential World Cup?

15. Which former England player died at Keighley, Yorkshire on January 22, 1978?

1	2	3	4	5	6	7	8	9	10	11	12	13	14	15
10	9	8	7	6	5	4	3	2	1	15	14	13	12	11

Answers: **1.** Birmingham **2.** A left-hand bowler's off-break to a right-hand batsman. **3.** Geoff Boycott **4.** Mark Burgess **5.** Melbourne **6.** 65 **7.** Alan Knott (252) **8.** Oxford and Cambridge **9.** Jamaica **10.** 4¼ in. or 108 mm **11.** Herbert Sutcliffe **12.** Clive Lloyd **13.** 758–8 dec. Kingston, 1954/55 **14.** England and West Indies **15.** The Oval.

6

He led New Zealand to a memorable feat in 1956 – who is he and what was it?

7

1. With which two Test batting feats did this player write himself into the record books in 1976?
2. Who bowled himself into the record books in the same series and how?
3. Who won the series and by what score?

Puzzle C

Cap that!

Which two Test players have also been capped for England at soccer since the War?

Puzzle D

What makes Bob Abel, Plum Warner and Len Hutton an exclusive trio of England openers?

8

1. He's Australia's second most prolific Test run-maker behind Bradman— can you name him?
2. What's his Test tally?
3. When was the only occasion he captained Australia?

Puzzle E

It's strange but:
1. Young players have made Test debuts at . . . .
2. Common players have appeared at . . . .
3. And they still use a round ball at . . . .

Puzzle F

Who's this?
1. Bespectacled right-hand batsman.
2. Topped the English first-class averages in 1976.
3. Hit his highest Test score of 274 against England at Edgbaston in 1971.

Go for the runs!

1. Against which team did David Gower hit his maiden Test century for England?
2. Was Australia's Sheffield Shield competition started in 1882, 1892 or 1902?
3. Which two brothers opened the batting for England in the 1880 Test against Australia?
4. What was Australia's winning margin in the 1975/76 series against the West Indies?
5. Who captained England on the 1972/73 tour of India and Pakistan?
6. In which series did New Zealand score her first Test win over England?
7. What is the Australian term for 'extras'?
8. What was special about England's series win in India in 1976/77?
9. In which year did Pakistan win her first Test in Australia—in 1975, 1976 or 1977?
10. Colin McDonald and Jim Burke opened the batting for which country?

11. How many runs did Sir Donald Bradman need in his last innings to finish with a Test average of 100?
12. How many dismissals did Australia's Wally Grout make in his Test career?
13. What is the highest Test stand by England against Australia and who made it?
14. Which West Indian made 200 and 114 not out against New Zealand on his Test debut in 1971?

15. In which Test did the scores run like this: Australia 63 and 122? England 101 and 77?

1	2	3	4	5	6	7	8	9	10	11	12	13	14	15
9	1	2	8	6	7	5	4	3	15	14	13	12	11	10

Answers: 1. 1892 2. W. G. and E. Grace 3. 1976 4. It was her first series win in India since 1934 5. Sundries 6. Tony Lewis 7. England's 1978 winter tour 8. 5–1 9. New Zealand, summer 1978 10. The first Ashes Test, The Oval, 1882 11. Lawrence Rowe 12. 382 by Hutton and Leyland for the 2nd wicket at The Oval in 1938 13. 187 14. Four (instead he got a duck) 15. Australia.

9

1. This stumping broke a wicket-keeping record —who, what where and when?
2. Who was the batsman out?

Puzzle G

What are the forenames of the following Test players?

1. . . . . Viswanath (India).

2. . . . . .Serjeant (Australia).

3. . . . . Rashid (Pakistan).

4. . . . . Bacher (South Africa).

5. . . . . Garner (West Indies).

6. . . . . Hendrick (England).

Go for the runs!

Quick 1 Singles

1. Jim Laker came out of retirement to play for which county?
2. Who is the West Indies' second leading Test run-maker after Gary Sobers?
3. What is the more common name for what the M.C.C. used to call the 'fast-leg theory'?
4. Who retired in 1964 never having lost a Test rubber as Australia's captain against England?
5. Who made a record 85 consecutive Test appearances?
6. Is David Hookes a left or right-hand bat?
7. What is the block hole?
8. Who captained South Africa on the 1963/64 tour of Australia?
9. In which year did overarm bowling become accepted—in 1854, 1864 or 1874?
10. Who scored most runs in a first class career?

Score a 4

11. What is the lowest Test score and who scored it?
12. Who retired from first class cricket after captaining the West Indies 18 times between 1957 and 1960?
13. Which Australian captained England?
14. Who was the oldest man to play in a Test?

6 Hit

15. Who were the three Kerry Packer players who won a High Court action in England in 1978 against a ban from Test and county cricket?

1	2	3	4	5	6	7	8	9	10	11	12	13	14	15
11	13	12	10	9	8	1	4	5	7	15	14	2	3	6

Answers: **1.** The batsman's guard mark **2.** G. O. 'Gubby' Allen, who was born in Australia **3.** Wilfrid Rhodes, aged 52 for England v West Indies, 1929/30 **4.** Trevor Goddard **5.** 1864 **6.** Tony Greig, John Snow and Mike Procter **7.** Sir Jack Hobbs, 61,237 **8.** Left **9.** Sir Gary Sobers **10.** Richie Benaud **11.** Essex **12.** Bodyline **13.** Rohan Kanhai, 6,227 **14.** Gerry Alexander **15.** 26 by New Zealand v England in 1954/55.

10

A

1. Identify these three famous West Indians.
2. What were they popularly known as?
3. Which one set a Test record of five centuries in successive innings?
4. For which particular skill did 'A' keep his Test place during the 1947/48 tour by England?
5. Which player has the middle name de Courcy?
6. Who has hit most Test centuries?
7. Who was the only one to captain the West Indies?
8. Which two figured in the second highest all-time first-class partnership and what was it?
9. For which batting feat in 1930 is 'B' still second only behind Bradman?
10. For which feat did 'A' join Herbert Sutcliffe, Greg Chappell, Sunil Gavaskar and George Headley in an exclusive group of Test cricketers?

B

C

Go for the runs!

1. Who made his Test debut for the West Indies in 1957, replacing Sonny Ramadhin?
2. For which country is Gary Cosier a Test player?
3. At which English ground would you find the Radcliffe Road end?
4. Which competition succeeded the Plunket Shield as New Zealand's chief competition?
5. Which former England player had the Christian names Charles Burgess?
6. Which English competition was inaugurated in 1963?
7. By which name is Mansur Ali Khan better known?
8. Whose top score was 285 not out for England against the West Indies in 1957?
9. Name one of Keith Miller's State sides.
10. Who succeeded Graham Dowling as New Zealand captain?

11. Name England's six Test grounds.
12. Which current England Test player was born in Zambia?
13. Who captained the first M.C.C. team to India in 1926/27?
14. Which South African is now opening bat for Kerry Packer's W.S.C. Australian XI?

15. When was the last time two brothers played for England in the same Test and who were they?

1	2	3	4	5	6	7	8	9	10	11	12	13	14	15
8	7	6	15	14	13	12	1	2	3	4	5	10	11	9

Answers: 1. Peter May 2. New South Wales or Victoria 3. Bev Congdon 4. Lord's; The Oval; Old Trafford, Manchester; Headingley, Leeds; Trent Bridge, Nottingham; Edgbaston, Birmingham 5. Phil Edmonds 6. Trent Bridge 7. Australia 8. Lance Gibbs 9. Peter and Derek Richardson, v West Indies, Trent Bridge, 1957 10. A. E. R. Gilligan 11. Kepler Wessels 12. The Nawab of Pataudi (jun) 13. The Gillette Cup 14. C. B. Fry 15. The Shell Cup.

Go for the runs!

1. Which famous Australian made his highest score of 300 not out against Sussex in 1899?
2. Name a former England captain who was born at Pudsey in Yorkshire.
3. Who sponsors Test matches in England?
4. Who leads England's Test batting averages overall?
5. For which skill was W. A. Oldfield a renowned Australian player?
6. Which former England Test player has the Christian name initials G. A. R.?
7. Whose 176 helped New Zealand to a thrilling finish against England at Trent Bridge in 1973?
8. Which West Indian was known as 'Electric Heels' for his fielding?
9. What type of spin bowler was Richie Benaud?
10. For which English county did Ken Barrington play?

11. What is the name of Johannesburg's Test ground?
12. Who holds the record for the fastest Test century by an Englishman?
13. What is Pakistan's lowest Test score?
14. Name Pakistan's four Test-playing Mohammad brothers.

15. Who topped the batting averages in Australia's 1953 tour of England—and what was peculiar about the feat?

1	2	3	4	5	6	7	8	9	10	11	12	13	14	15
7	6	1	2	3	11	15	14	13	5	10	9	8	4	12

Answers: **1.** Cornhill Insurance **2.** Herbert Sutcliffe (60.73) **3.** Wicket-keeping **4.** Wazir, Hanif, Mushtaq and Sadiq **5.** Surrey **6.** Sir Len Hutton, Ray Illingworth **7.** Victor Trumper **8.** 87 v England, Lord's, 1954 **9.** Gilbert Jessop, 75 minutes v Australia, 1902 **10.** Wanderers Ground **11.** Tony Lock **12.** W. A. Johnston with 102—he was a tail-end batsman who was not out 16 times in 17 innings **13.** Leg-spinner **14.** Learie Constantine **15.** Bev Congdon—but New Zealand were narrowly beaten.

Go for the runs!

Quick 1 Singles

1. Which famous Yorkshire and England bowler died in 1973?
2. Where would you find the Kennington Oval?
3. For which country did Johnny Waite keep wicket?
4. Which is the only English ground where play in a Test has been abandoned without a ball being bowled?
5. Which Australian state side plays at Brisbane?
6. Bobby Simpson was the first Test victim of which South African bowler?
7. Who established himself as one of Australia's most successful opening bats in 66 Tests between 1963 and 1976?
8. Which famous English batsman was known as 'Croucher'?
9. Who captained Pakistan between 1969 and 1975?
10. Who scored 291 against England at The Oval in 1976?

Score a 4

11. In which year did South Africa gain her first Test win in England?
12. Which English player was flown out to Australia in 1958/59 to bolster the injury-hit M.C.C. side?
13. Which England captain was drowned in a shipping accident in 1930?
14. For which injured England player was Basil D'Oliveira the replacement before England cancelled the 1968 tour of South Africa?

6 Hit

15. Who were the five players who scored centuries in Australia's largest Test total of 758–8 dec. v the West Indies in 1955?

1	2	3	4	5	6	7	8	9	10	11	12	13	14	15
7	6	10	9	8	15	14	13	5	4	3	1	2	11	12

Answers: **1.** Ted Dexter **2.** J. W. H. T. Douglas **3.** 1935 **4.** Viv Richards (West Indies) **5.** Intikhab Alam **6.** London **7.** Wilfrid Rhodes **8.** Queensland **9.** Old Trafford, Manchester (twice, in 1890 and 1938) **10.** South Africa **11.** Tom Cartwright **12.** C. McDonald (127), N. Harvey (204), K. Miller (109), R. Archer (128) and R. Benaud (121). **13.** Gilbert Jessop **14.** Ian Redpath **15.** Mike Procter.

A

B

How's That?

1. Who were the successful bowlers in these England v Australia clashes?
2. Who won the 1954/55 series?
3. Who won the 1964 series?
4. What were the outstanding batting performances of the fourth Test in 1964?
5. Who are the batsman and wicket-keeper in picture A?

1. Who is this famous Australian all-rounder?
2. Which two State sides did he play for?
3. How many Test centuries did he score?
4. How many Test wickets did he take?
5. Against which English county did he make his highest first-class score?
6. After which Australian adventurers was he named?

Puzzle H

Who's this?

1. Made his Test debut in 1964.

2. Totalled 5,187 runs from 72 Tests including a top score of 196 at Adelaide in 1972/73.

3. Lost his first Test as skipper but won 15 out of 30 before standing down.

Puzzle J

Which of the following Test cricketers fits all the clues?

Mushtaq Mohammad, Clive Lloyd, Barry Richards, Geoff Howarth, Greg Chappell, Dayle Hadlee.

1. Right-hand bat.

2. Joined the Packer circus.

3. Captained his country.

4. Has a younger Test-playing brother.

Go for the runs!

1. Who scored the highest individual Test score ?
2. What is it ?
3. And against whom did he score it?
4. What's a pair?
5. Which State side has won the Sheffield Shield most times—Western Australia, New South Wales or Queensland?
6. Which Test cricketer 'died for four seconds' in a match in 1973 ?
7. Who was the bowler who felled him?
8. What is the lowest Test score by England?
9. In which year did the tradition of the Ashes start?
10. Who captained the West Indies on their 1978/79 tour of India?

11. Who is the only player to have been given out in a Test match for obstruction of the field?
12. Who ended up with a Test average of 99.94?
13. Who invented the googly?
14. Who apart from Geoff Boycott scored his 100th first class century during 1977?

15. Whose 905 runs in a Test series is still an English record?

1	2	3	4	5	6	7	8	9	10	11	12	13	14	15
11	10	15	14	13	12	9	7	6	1	2	3	8	4	5

Answers: **1.** Alvin Kallicharran **2.** Sir Len Hutton, England v South Africa, The Oval, 1951. **3.** Sir Don Bradman **4.** John Edrich **5.** Wally Hammond, England v Australia, 1928/29 **6.** 1882 **7.** 45 v Australia, Sydney, 1886/87 **8.** B. J. T. Bosanquet **9.** Peter Lever (England) **10.** 365 not out **11.** Sir Gary Sobers **12.** Ewan Chatfield (New Zealand) **13.** New South Wales **14.** Where a batsman scores nought in each innings **15.** Pakistan (1957/58).

Name the grounds

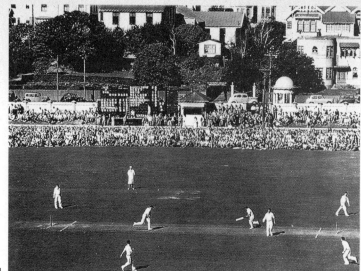

1

2

3

Puzzle K

Which of the following Test cricketers fits all the clues?

Mike Procter, Sir Gary Sobers, John Edrich, Geoff Boycott, Colin Cowdrey, Bobby Simpson.
1. Right-hand bat.
2. Has captained his country.
3. More than 80 Test appearances.
4. Scored his 100th century in 1973.

Puzzle L

Five post-War England players have scored centuries on their Test debut – how many can you name?

1. . . . .
2. . . . .
3. . . . .
4. . . . .
5. . . . .

Go for the runs!

Quick 1 Singles

1. Who was Australia's youngest Test captain?
2. For which country did George Headley play?
3. Who has scored most centuries in first class cricket?
4. Who held the Ashes after Australia's 1972 tour of England?
5. For which country did Bert Sutcliffe play?
6. Which cricketer has the Christian names Wesley Winfield?
7. What is a maiden over?
8. Which English county has its headquarters at Trent Bridge?
9. Which Indian Test player was sacked by Northamptonshire in 1978?
10. Complete this famous West Indian bowling partnership—Ramadhin and ....?

Score a 4

11. What and when was Australia's lowest Test total against England?
12. What is John Edrich's highest Test score for England?
13. The stand of 323 by Hobbs and Rhodes at Melbourne in 1911/12 is still an English record—what is it?
14. In which year did India beat England in a Test for the first time?

6 Hit

15. Which player holds the record for the fastest Test 'double' of 1,000 runs and 100 wickets?

1	2	3	4	5	6	7	8	9	10	11	12	13	14	15
5	6	7	8	9	10	11	15	14	13	12	1	2	3	4

Answers: **1.** 310 not out (against New Zealand at Leeds 1965—also his highest first class score) **2.** The highest first-wicket stand against Australia **3.** 1952 **4.** India's Vinoo Mankad, in 23 Tests **5.** Ian Craig, 22 **6.** West Indies **7.** Sir Jack Hobbs, 197 **8.** England retained them after a 2–2 draw **9.** New Zealand **10.** Wes Hall **11.** One in which the batsman scores no runs **12.** 36 at Edgbaston in 1902 **13.** Valentine **14.** Bishen Bedi **15.** Nottinghamshire.

Go for the runs!

1. Which West Indian island plays at Port of Spain?
2. Whose planned tour of England in 1970 was called off?
3. Where would you watch a Shell Cup match?
4. Who has taken most Test wickets for India?
5. Which country first won a Test rubber in the West Indies?
6. Which was Ian Chappell's last Test as Australia's captain?
7. Which Englishman has bowled most Test balls?
8. Who were the beaten finalists in the 1975 Prudential World Cup?
9. Where are Duleep Trophy and Irani Cup matches played?
10. Which Australian last captained a Test side in South Africa?

11. For which trophy do Australia and the West Indies play?
12. What was remarkable about the result of the 1977 Centenary Test between England and Australia?
13. Who was the last bowler to do the hat-trick in a Test match?
14. When did India first beat England in a Test match?

15. What record does P. G. H. Fender hold?

1	2	3	4	5	6	7	8	9	10	11	12	13	14	15
9	10	11	12	13	1	14	15	8	7	6	5	4	3	2

Answers: **1.** The last (fourth) Test in England, 1975 **2.** The fastest century (35 minutes) **3.** 1952 at Madras **4.** P. J. Petherick, New Zealand v Pakistan, 1976/77 **5.** Australia won by the same margin—45 runs—as in the first Test 100 years earlier. **6.** The Sir Frank Worrell Trophy **7.** Bill Lawry **8.** India **9.** Trinidad **10.** South Africa **11.** New Zealand **12.** Bishen Bedi **13.** Australia, 1954/55 **14.** Derek Underwood, 18,979 **15.** Australia.

14

His feat in the 1973 English season hadn't been achieved since 1938—who is he and what was it?

15

1. Who is this former England captain?
2. For which series did he first take the job?
3. How many Test centuries did he score?
4. What, where and when was his top Test score?

Puzzle M

Who's this?
1. Born Guyana, 1935.

2. Captained his country in 13 Tests.

3. Played in 79 Tests, scoring 6,227 runs.

Puzzle N

1. Which West Indian's day wasn't in this England captain's month?

2. Flour and flower . . . clues to two Australian quickies.

Go for the runs!

Quick **1** Singles

1. What is the distance between bowling and popping creases?
2. What is a 'yorker'?
3. Who captained New Zealand to her first ever Test win over India in 1967/68?
4. Who made South Africa's highest individual Test score?
5. What do the initials I.C.C. stand for?
6. What position is taken up by the umpire standing at the batsman's end?
7. In which county was Jim Laker born?
8. At which Test ground would you find the Warwick Road end?
9. For which country did Lindsay Kline play?
10. How did Australian bowler Ian Meckiff cause such a controversy?

Score a **4**

11. In which season did England first play six home Tests and why?
12. Why was MCC's projected tour of South Africa in 1968/69 called off?
13. In which country would you find the Queen's Park Oval?
14. What was Glenn Turner's outstanding performance in New Zealand's Test win over Australia at Christchurch in 1974?

6 Hit

15. When was the last 'timeless' Test, who played in it and how and why did it end?

1	2	3	4	5	6	7	8	9	10	11	12	13	14	15
11	10	9	15	14	13	12	1	2	3	4	8	7	6	5

Answers: **1.** Old Trafford, Manchester **2.** Australia **3.** His action was said to constitute a throw **4.** In 1965, against New Zealand and South Africa, to allow attractive teams such as the West Indies to come more often **5.** In England's 1938/39 tour of South Africa when the fifth Test was given up after 10 days because the MCC team had to catch their ship home, still 42 runs short of victory **6.** A century in each innings **7.** Trinidad **8.** Because the South Africans wouldn't allow England Test player Basil D'Oliveira to tour because of his colour **9.** Graham Dowling **10.** A full-length ball which pitches in or around the popping crease **11.** 48 inches (122 cm) **12.** Yorkshire **13.** Square leg **14.** International Cricket Conference **15.** Graeme Pollock, 274 v Australia, Durban, 1969/70.

Name the Test batsmen

Puzzle P

1. Who is the only player to have scored a century in each innings on his Test debut?

2. Who is the only cricketer to have been given out 'handled the ball' in a Test match?

3. Who is the only South African to have taken a hat-trick in a Test match?

1

2

3

4

Go for the runs!

Quick
1
Singles

1. What is the signal for a wide?
2. What is the highest one-innings score in a Test match?
3. Who was the only bowler to take 100 wickets in the 1977 English season?
4. Who was Australia's youngest Test player?
5. In which year did the West Indies begin playing Test cricket—1928, 1938 or 1948?
6. Who won Australia's first Test series in the West Indies in 1954/55?
7. Who is the only Australian to have scored a century against England in his first Test as captain?
8. Is Derek Underwood a right or left-arm bowler?
9. Which honour did Sir Learie Constantine receive in 1969?
10. Which Test side toured India in 1978/79?

Score a
4

11. What was Australian Test captain Bill Lawry's occupation outside cricket?
12. In which decade were the number of stumps at either end increased from two to three?
13. What is the name of Brisbane's Test ground?
14. Who captained Australia between 1930 and 1934?

6
Hit

15. How and when did Geoff Boycott end a 10-year run during England's 1978/79 tour of Australia?

1	2	3	4	5	6	7	8	9	10	11	12	13	14	15
10	9	8	14	13	12	11	7	6	5	15	1	2	3	4

Answers: **1.** Between 1770 and 1780 **2.** The Gabba **3.** W. M. Woodfull **4.** He scored a duck in the fourth Test—his first in 67 Tests since August, 1969 (v New Zealand) **5.** West Indies **6.** A life peerage **7.** Left arm **8.** Gloucestershire's Mike Procter **9.** 903–7 dec, by England v Australia, The Oval, 1938 **10.** Both arms held apart **11.** Graham Yallop, 1978 **12.** Australia, 3–0 **13.** 1928 **14.** Ian Craig, 17 **15.** A plumber.

Go for the runs!

1. What is a 'plumb' wicket?
2. Who took the first M.C.C. team to Australia?
3. Against which country did Glenn Turner make his Test debut for New Zealand?
4. Who is Australia's leading Test wicket-keeper?
5. Who had the Christian names John Berry?
6. For which West Indian island did Wes Hall play?
7. Which cricketer was Christened to give him the initials of a famous club?
8. Is Barry Richards a right- or left-hand bat?
9. What is a 'king-pair'?
10. Who captained the 1970 South Africans against Australia?

11. When and against whom did Ken Barrington score his first Test century in England?
12. Who holds the record for most Test wickets by a spinner in an England-Australian rubber?
13. What and when was England's lowest Test total against the West Indies?
14. Who bequeathed the Ashes to the M.C.C.?

15. Who is the only player to have scored a century in each innings of a Test match TWICE in the same series?

1	2	3	4	5	6	7	8	9	10	11	12	13	14	15
10	9	8	15	14	13	12	7	6	5	1	2	3	4	11

Answers: **1.** 1964 against Australia at Old Trafford with 256 **2.** England's Jim Laker (46 in 1956) **3.** 71 at Old Trafford, 1976 **4.** Lord Darnley (formerly the Hon. Ivo Bligh) who captained the England side who regained the Ashes in 1883 **5.** Ali Bacher **6.** When a batsman is out first ball for a duck in each innings of a match **7.** Right **8.** West Indies in 1968/69 **9.** P. F. 'Plum' Warner **10.** A perfect batting wicket unaffected by rain or wear **11.** Clyde Walcott, West Indies v Australia, 1954/55 **12.** Michael Colin Cowdrey **13.** Barbados **14.** Sir Jack Hobbs **15.** Richie Benaud, 248.

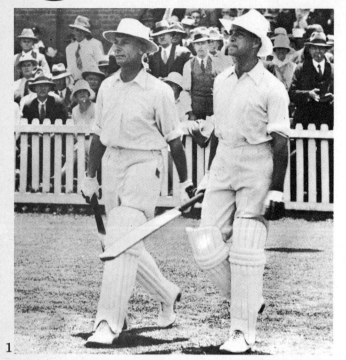

1

Who make up these famous partnerships?

3

2

Puzzle Q

Who are these cricketers?

1. The Doctor
2. Polly
3. Tiger
4. The Master
5. Barnacle
6. Sunny
7. The Noob
8. Lord Ted
9. Dolly
10. Tommo
11. Tufty
12. Kipper
13. The Don
14. Tich
15. Fiery Fred
16. Froggy

Go for the runs!

1. Which cricketer has the Christian names Alan Philip Eric?
2. Which English umpire is known as 'Dicky'?
3. Who succeeded Bobby Simpson as Australian skipper in 1968?
4. What was the main punishment for the English players who joined Kerry Packer's World Series Cricket?
5. Who skippered the only unbeaten Australian tour side of England?
6. Which Englishman has scored most runs for his country?
7. What colour caps do Australian Test players wear?
8. In which year was amateur status abolished in England, in 1962, 1963 or 1964?
9. In which city would you find Australia's Oval?
10. Who won the 1978/79 series between India and the West Indies?

11. Who made the highest individual first-class score?
12. Who is the only English batsman to have averaged 100 in an English season?
13. What is the lowest Test score by India?
14. By what margin did the West Indies win the 1975 Prudential World Cup?

15. Which batsman was in for 97 minutes before scoring his first run during an England-Australia series?

1	2	3	4	5	6	7	8	9	10	11	12	13	14	15
12	13	14	15	11	10	9	8	7	6	5	1	2	3	4

Answers: **1.** Geoff Boycott, 1971 **2.** 42 v England, Lord's 1974 **3.** 17 **4.** Godfrey Evans (England) Adelaide, 1946/47 **5.** Hanif Mohammad, 499, Karachi v Bahawalpur, 1958/59 **6.** India, 1–0 **7.** Adelaide **8.** 1963 **9.** Green **10.** Colin Cowdrey, 7,624 **11.** Sir Donald Bradman, 1948 **12.** Alan Knott **13.** Harold Bird **14.** Bill Lawry **15.** They were banned from Test cricket.

1

2

3

4

1. Who is this famous player?
2. Which Test milestone was he the first to pass as an all-rounder?
3. True or false: He never lost a rubber in 28 Tests as captain.

1. This was one shot of a memorable fourth Test innings at Manchester in 1961—who's the batsman?
2. What was the stand he figured in and who was his partner?
3. What happened as a result and how did it affect the series?

Puzzle R   Which famous Yorkshire captain toured New Zealand and never scored a single run?

Go for the runs!

1. P. B. H. are the Christian name initials of which cricketer?
2. Who scored a century on his Test debut for England in 1880?
3. Who was England's captain in the 'bodyline' series against Australia in 1932/33?
4. What is the first innings lead required to ask the opposition to follow-on in a Test match?
5. At which ground would you find Old Father Time?
6. In which country would you find the Eden Park ground?
7. Where is Ian Botham's birthplace—Surrey, Cheshire or Somerset?
8. Which county apart from Yorkshire did Freddie Trueman play for?
9. What do the initials T.C.C.B. stand for?
10. What is a bump ball?

11. Name the three Kent and England Test wicket-keepers?
12. Who topped the Australian domestic batting averages in 1976/77?
13. Who was the last Englishman to score a century on his Test debut?
14. Who was the youngest Test player and how old was he?

15. Name the six England players who had signed for Kerry Packer by the end of 1978.

1	2	3	4	5	6	7	8	9	10	11	12	13	14	15
11	10	9	15	14	13	12	4	3	2	1	5	6	7	8

Answers: **1.** Les Ames, Godfrey Evans, Alan Knott **2.** Where the ball is driven hard into the ground and when caught by a close-in fielder gives the appearance of a catch. **3.** Test and County Cricket Board **4.** Derbyshire **5.** David Hookes (78.80) **6.** Frank Hayes v West Indies, Lord's 1973 **7.** Mushtaq Mohammad (15) **8.** Tony Greig, Alan Knott, Bob Woolmer, Derek Underwood, Dennis Amiss, John Snow **9.** Douglas Jardine **10.** W. G. Grace **11.** Peter May **12.** Cheshire **13.** New Zealand (Auckland) **14.** Lord's **15.** 200.

21

Deadly Duo's

Pair up these famous Test bowling
partnerships and say who they are.

2

3

1

4

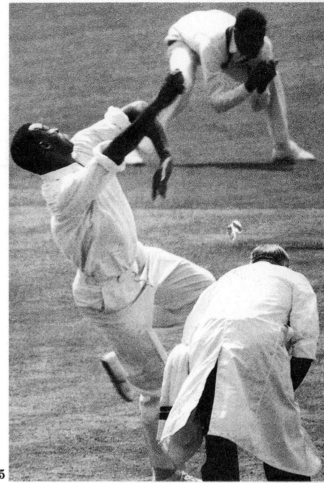

5

Puzzle S

Which of the following Test bowlers fits all the clues?

Dennis Lillee, John Snow, Jeff Thomson, Len Pascoe, Derek Underwood, Bob Willis.

1. Right-armer.
2. Plays for Kerry Packer circus.
3. Played in the England v. Australia 1975 series.
4. Took 31 wickets in the 1972 series between England and Australia.

6

The left hand page

A. Four left-handers have scored 5,000 runs or more in Test cricket – how many can you name?

1. . . . .
2. . . . .
3. . . . .
4. . . . .

B. Four England left-handers have scored 1,500 runs or more in Test matches since the War – can you name them?

1. . . . .
2. . . . .
3. . . . .
4. . . . .

C. Which left-hand batsman has scored most runs in Test matches?

D. Which left-hand bowler has taken most Test wickets?

E. Who's the odd batsman out?

Sadiq Mohammad
Clive Lloyd
David Gower
Glenn Turner
Younis Ahmed
Alvin Kallicharran

F. Who's the odd bowler out?

Derek Underwood
Gary Gilmour
Phil Edmonds
Bishen Bedi
Max Walker
John Lever

G. Who's this Yorkshire and England all rounder?   **G.**

Find the player

Unscramble the letters to find the well known Test players.

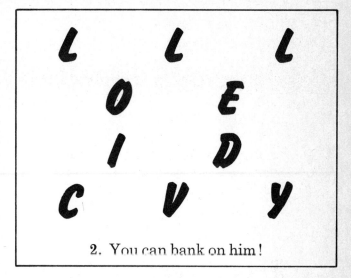

1. Has an equally devastating namesake !

2. You can bank on him !

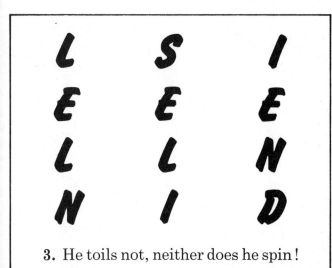

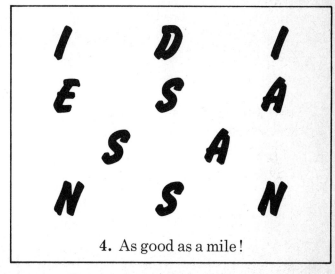

3. He toils not, neither does he spin !

4. As good as a mile !

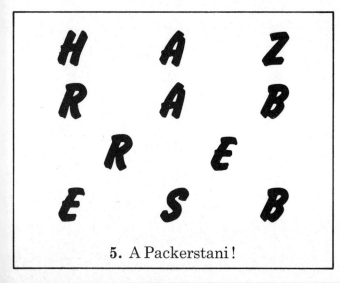

5. A Packerstani !

6. Bye-Bye !

Go for the runs!

1. For which country did Seymour Nurse play?
2. How did the term 'a pair'—where a batsman is out for nought in each innings—originate?
3. In which English city would you find the Old Trafford ground?
4. In which year was Sunday league cricket introduced in England?
5. How was the pitch marked out before the use of whitewash?
6. Why did Colin Cowdrey acquire a car number plate which included the figure 307?
7. Which cricketer's Christian names are Isaac Vivian Alexander?
8. What is the signal for a no-ball?
9. Is Colin Bland a New Zealand, South African or Australian Test player?
10. For which country does Allan Border play?

11. Which English batsman made his highest Test score against Pakistan at Karachi in 1961/62?
12. Who was the first Englishman to score a century in each innings of a Test match against Australia?
13. Up to the end of 1978, who was the last player to score a century on his Test debut?
14. Which wicket-keeper holds the record for most dismissals in a Test match?

15. How long was the slowest Test century and who scored it?

1	2	3	4	5	6	7	8	9	10	11	12	13	14	15
13	14	15	12	11	10	9	1	2	3	4	8	7	6	5

Answers: **1.** One arm outstretched to the side **2.** South African **3.** Australia **4.** Ted Dexter (205) **5.** Nine hours 17 minutes by Mudassar for Pakistan v England, December, 1977 **6.** Gil Langley, nine against England at Lord's, 1956 **7.** Pakistan's Javed Miandad, against New Zealand, 1976/77 **8.** Herbert Sutcliffe, Melbourne, 1924/25 **9.** Viv Richards **10.** It was his highest first-class score **11.** The turf was cut **12.** 1969 **13.** West Indies **14.** It's short for 'a pair of spectacles', i.e. 00 **15.** Manchester.

Place the fielders (for a right-hand batsman)

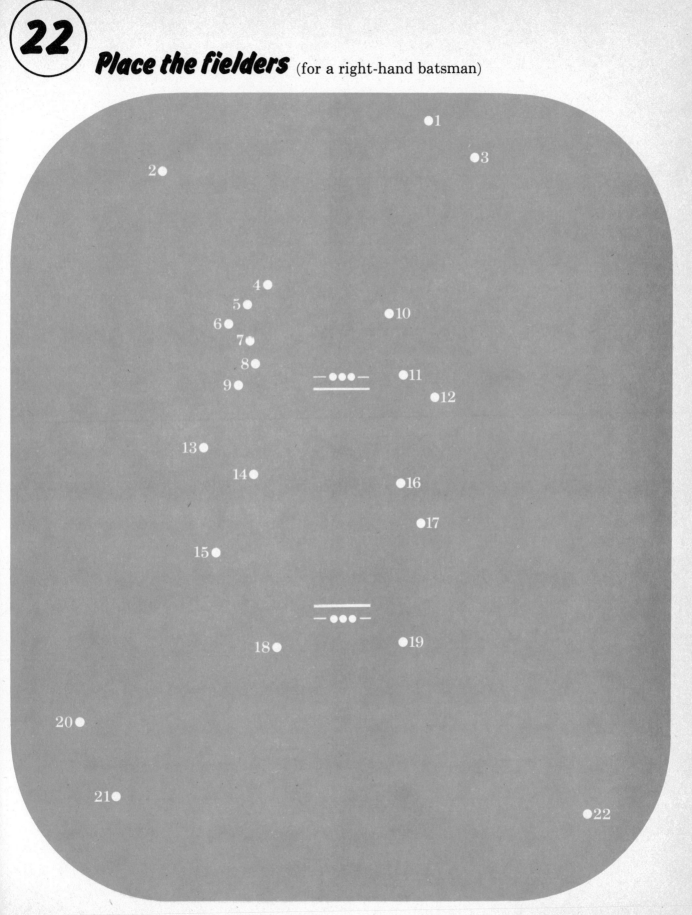

Name the Test batsmen

1

2

Puzzle T

Who's this?

1. Right-arm fast bowler for Yorkshire, Derbyshire and England.
2. The second most successful Test bowler of all time with 307 wickets from 67 Tests.
3. Now a member of the BBC radio commentary team.

Puzzle U

Who are these cricketers?

1. The Guvnor

2. The Big Ship

3. The Governor General

4. Mr Smith

5. Davo

6. Lindy

7. Iron Bottom

8. Big Bird

3

Oh Brother!

Pair up these brothers and say who they are

2

1

3

25

1. Which Test series is in progress here?
2. Who is being dismissed, by whom and off whose bowling?
3. How did this scene have an action replay and when?
4. Who won the series and by what margin?

1. What and where was this match and who is the batsman?
2. What was his highest score in this match and in which innings?
3. How was he out here and in which innings?
4. In which match did he score his next century against the same opposition?

Name the Test batsmen

1

2

28

1. Identify these former England captains.
2. How many were born in England?
3. Which was born in Milan?
4. Which was born in India?
5. What are the native countries of the others?
6. Which one lost the Ashes?
7. Which one never captained England at home?
8. Which is the most recent England captain?

1

2

Puzzle V

Fill in the names (across) of England's 1978/79 Australian touring party to find the name (down) of a well-known Australian player.

3

5

4

Puzzle W

Who's this?

1. Made his debut for the Leeward Islands in 1971.
2. Scored two double centuries against England in 1976.
3. Now divides his time between English county cricket with Somerset and playing for Kerry Packer's World Series Cricket.

29 Deadly Duo's

Name the bowling pairs.

1

2

3

4

5

6

2

3

1

Puzzle X

Who's this?

1. Slow left-arm former Test bowler.
2. Ranks as the world's third most successful fielder with 830 catches in career of 26 seasons.

1. With what record did this bowler burst into English first-class cricket in 1963?
2. How many Test appearances has he made?
3. How many Test wickets has he taken?
4. What is his best Test return?
5. Why was his Test career halted in 1977?

Puzzle Y

There have been six instances of fathers and sons playing for England – how many can you name?

1. . . . .
2. . . . .
3. . . . .
4. . . . .
5. . . . .
6. . . . .

Puzzle Z

Who's this?
1. Right-arm fast bowler for New South Wales, Queensland and Australia.

2. Terrorised batsmen in his first tour to England in 1948, taking 27 wickets.

3. Appeared in 61 Tests, taking 228 wickets.

Go for the runs!

1. Who was England's manager on their 1978/79 tour of Australia?
2. What is the umpire's signal for a bye?
3. Who succeeded Richie Benaud as Australia's captain?
4. Which is Clive Lloyd's home country in the West Indies?
5. For which English county did Australia's Graham McKenzie play?
6. Who was born at Fitzwilliam, Yorkshire?
7. What is the scorer's sign for a no-ball?
8. Which was Mike Denness's last Test as England captain?
9. For which series did the teams wear 'wattle gold and strawberry mousse'?
10. Who topped England's batting averages agains the West Indies in 1976?

11. In which year did New Zealand score her first Test victory over Australia?
12. Who was England's reserve wicket-keeper on the 1977/78 tour of Pakistan and New Zealand?
13. Why did the third Test between England and Australia in 1975 end on a Monday?
14. What and when was England player Alan Knott's highest Test score?

15. Who was top scorer in the semi-final match between England and Australia in the 1975 World Cup?

1	2	3	4	5	6	7	8	9	10	11	12	13	14	15
9	8	7	6	1	2	3	4	5	13	15	14	12	11	10

Answers: **1.** Leicestershire **2.** Geoff Boycott **3.** A dot with a circle round it **4.** The first Test against Australia, Edgbaston, 1975 **5.** Kerry Packer's 1978 WSC matches between Australia and the West Indies **6.** Guyana **7.** Bobby Simpson **8.** One arm raised above the head **9.** Doug Insole **10.** Gary Gilmour (Australia) 28 not out **11.** 116 against the West Indies (1976) and Pakistan (1971) **12.** Because vandals dug up the Headingley pitch, making the final day's play impossible. **13.** John Edrich, 48.33 **14.** Kent's Paul Downton **15.** 1974 at Christchurch.

32

Past and present Test captains

1

3

4

2

Go for the runs!

1. Where would you be watching a Shell Shield match?
2. Who captained England for the first match against Pakistan in 1954?
3. What was the score in New Zealand's Test series in England in 1978?
4. What do W. R. Hammond's initials stand for?
5. What is the number of Kerry Packer's Australia television channel?
6. Who was the last player to do 'the double' of 100 wickets and 1,000 runs in an English season?
7. Which former New Zealand international is now a rugby international?
8. Which country toured England in 1976?
9. Who won the women's World Cup in 1977?
10. Who last won the English county championship three times in a row?

11. Which wicket-keeper has taken most Test catches and what's his tally?
12. Which was John Edrich's only Test as England captain?
13. Which two countries play for the W. J. Jordan Trophy?
14. What was Mike Denness's first match as England captain?

15. What is the highest score by a player on his Test debut and can you name him?

1	2	3	4	5	6	7	8	9	10	11	12	13	14	15
15	14	13	12	11	10	9	8	7	6	5	4	3	2	1

Answers: **1.** 287, by R. E. Foster, for England v Australia, Sydney 1903/4 **2.** The first Prudential one-day international v West Indies, 1973 **3.** England and New Zealand **4.** Fourth Test v Australia, 1974/75 (when Mike Denness dropped himself) **5.** Alan Knott (England) 233 **6.** Yorkshire 1966–68 **7.** England **8.** West Indies **9.** Brian McKechnie **10.** F. J. Titmus (Middlesex) 1967 **11.** Channel 9 **12.** Walter Reginald **13.** 3–0 to England **14.** Len Hutton **15.** West Indies.

Go for the runs!

1. How many balls are there in a usual Australian over?
2. Who was the controversial appointment as Yorkshire captain for the 1979 season?
3. Who are the Kiwis?
4. Where was cricket's first floodlit match played?
5. Who returned figures of 16 for 137 on his Test debut in 1972?
6. What is the maximum number of overs permitted for a side batting first in the English county championship?
7. What height from the ground are a full-size set of stumps?
8. What is the signal for a six-hit?
9. Who has made most Test appearances for England?
10. Whose autobiography is entitled 'I Don't Bruise Easily'?

11. Who was the youngest Englishman·to make his Test debut?
12. Under what circumstances may captains agree to play without bails?
13. What is the Australian term for a googly?
14. What is the largest ever Test defeat?

15. For which Indian captain was 1971 a memorable year and why?

1	2	3	4	5	6	7	8	9	10	11	12	13	14	15
14	13	12	11	2	1	6	5	4	3	15	10	9	8	7

Answers: **1.** 100 **2.** Bob Massie (for Australia v England) **3.** Brian Close **4.** Colin Cowdrey, 114 (plus 4 v World XI) **5.** Both arms raised above the head **6.** 28 inches (71 cm) **7.** Ajit Wadekar, because his Test teams beat England in England for the first time and scored their first Test and series win over the West Indies. **8.** An innings and 579 runs, suffered by Australia v England, The Oval, 1938 **9.** A bosie (after B. J. T. Bosanquet, who is credited with inventing it) **10.** In high winds **11.** Melbourne, 1978—a Packer match **12.** The New Zealanders **13.** John Hampshire **14.** Eight **15.** Brian Close, at 18.

What's the connection?

1

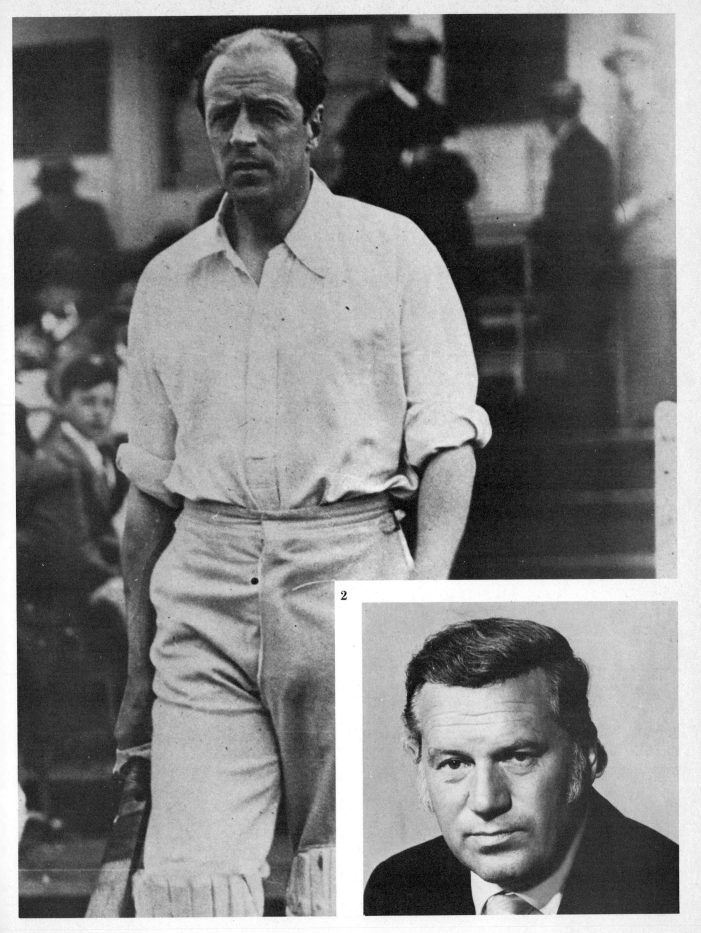

2

Go for the runs!

1. Which Australian state side has its HQ at Perth?
2. Who was the Grand Old Man of English cricket?
3. What was Pakistan's surprise performance in the 1954 tour of England?
4. Which England bowler was controversially sacked by Yorkshire in 1958?
5. For which West Indian island did Alf Valentine play?
6. Who captained England for three Tests against Australia in 1975?
7. For which English county does Zaheer Abbas play?
8. Which former Australian captain played two seasons with Somerset?
9. By which name was O'Neill Gordon Smith better known?
10. What is the signal for a leg bye?

11. Who was England's defeated captain in the 1961/62 series in India?
12. What would be unusual now about the style of former England player William Clarke?
13. Who is the oldest of Pakistan's Test-playing Mohammad brothers?
14. Which renowned Indian leg-spin bowler made the first of 36 Test match appearances in 1951?

15. Who are the only three players to have scored six successive first class centuries?

1	2	3	4	5	6	7	8	9	10	11	12	13	14	15
10	12	8	6	4	2	13	7	5	3	15	14	1	9	11

Answers: **1.** Wazir **2.** Tony Greig **3.** Raising a leg and touching the knee with the hand **4.** Jamaica **5.** Collie Smith (a brilliant West Indian Test player who was killed in a car accident in 1959) **6.** Johnny Wardle **7.** Greg Chappell **8.** They beat England in one Test and drew the series in their first visit **9.** S. P. Gupte **10.** Western Australia **11.** C. B. Fry (1901), Don Bradman (1938/39), Mike Procter (1970/71) **12.** W. G. Grace **13.** Gloucestershire **14.** He was an underarm bowler—and very successful! **15.** Ted Dexter.

Go for the runs!

Quick **1** Singles

1. Who captained New Zealand between 1956 and 1965?
2. What is a 'sticky dog'?
3. What were the so-called 'timeless Tests'?
4. At which ground does England traditionally play her final home Test?
5. Where would you find the Imperial Cricket Memorial museum?
6. What does the term l.b.w. stand for?
7. Who captained Pakistan in the 1978 series against England?
8. For which country does Deryck Murray play?
9. Who was the first Englishman to score a Test century?
10. Who led the last unbeaten Australian Test side in England?

Score a **4**

11. Which was the only county side to beat the 1977 Australian tourists?
12. What was the winning target the West Indies set Australia in the 1975 World Cup final?
13. Which New Zealander made his Test debut playing for Australia in 1924?
14. Which Australian bowler took 14–90 in the first 'Ashes' Test at the Oval in 1882?

6 Hit

15. Who became known as 'Bedser's bunny' and why?

1	2	3	4	5	6	7	8	9	10	11	12	13	14	15
15	14	13	12	4	3	2	1	5	6	7	8	10	9	11

Answers: **1.** (WSC) West Indies **2.** Wasim Bari **3.** Leg before wicket **4.** Lord's **5.** W. G. Grace, 152 v Australia, 1880 **6.** Ian Chappell, 1975 **7.** Somerset (and the Minor Counties) **8.** 292 **9.** Frederick Spofforth **10.** Clarrie Grimmett **11.** Australian Test batsman Arthur Morris, because he was so often out to England bowler Alec Bedser **12.** The Oval **13.** Where a series was all square with one to play, it was usually agreed to play to a conclusion **14.** A rain-affected pitch which turns sticky drying out under the sun, causing the ball to jump unpredictably **15.** John Reid.

34

1. Who is this legendary batsman?
2. What was his nickname?
3. With which two players did he figure in stands of 323 and 172 respectively and what was the significance of each partnership?
4. Whose record did he pass for most first class centuries and how many did he go on to make?
5. Who eventually broke his record of 16 first class centuries in a season?
6. In which year did he die?

35

1. His Test performance at Lord's in 1972 has been bettered by only two other players—who is he and what was it?
2. How did that Test series end?

Puzzle AA

Who said the following of whom about what?

1. 'The whole thing was a set-up'.

2. 'An objectionable term, utterly foreign to cricket and designed to stir up strife.'

3. 'We intend to make them grovel.'

4. 'Mann's inhumanity to Mann.'

Go for the runs!

1. At which ground would you find the Mound stand?
2. What is 'a nightwatchman'?
3. Which cricketer has the middle name St. Aubrun?
4. Who made his Test debut for England at 33 in 1975?
5. By which name is the Cricketers' Almanack better known?
6. Who is Pakistan's leading Test run-maker?
7. What colour caps do England wear?
8. Who won the first Test match between England and Australia?
9. Where would you watch a Plunket Shield match?
10. Who dropped himself from Kerry Packer's World XI in 1978 because of poor form?

11. Which of the 1978/79 England Test batsmen bagged 'a pair' in his first Test?
12. Which is the world's largest cricket ground?
13. Who was known as 'the black Bradman'?
14. What was Sir Don Bradman's score in his final Test innings?

15. Who took Bradman's wicket in his final Test innings?

1	2	3	4	5	6	7	8	9	10	11	12	13	14	15
6	7	8	9	10	4	3	2	1	15	14	13	5	11	12

Answers: **1.** New Zealand **2.** Australia **3.** Navy blue **4.** Hanif Mohammad, 3,915 **5.** George Headley (West Indies) **6.** Lord's **7.** A tail-end batsman who comes in before close of play to guard against losing a more valuable wicket at that stage of play **8.** Sir Gary Sobers **9.** David Steele (v Australia) **10.** Wisden **11.** Nought **12.** England's Eric Hollies **13.** Melbourne **14.** Graham Gooch (v Australia, 1975) **15.** Tony Greig.

Go for the runs!

1. For which country would you have seen the bowling partnership of Adcock and Heine?
2. For which stroke is Denis Compton best remembered?
3. What is a googly?
4. Who has the Christian names Anderson Montgomery Everton?
5. What is the name of Kerry Packer's cricket circus?
6. Who captained the first England Test side in Australia in 1876/77?
7. At which ground would you find The Hill?
8. What is a 'beamer'?
9. Who is the leading Test wicket-taker?
10. What is his total?

11. What was unusual about C. L. Townsend's hat-trick for Gloucestershire v Somerset in 1893?
12. In which year did Sir Len Hutton make his Test debut?
13. Who was the first player to score 2,000 runs and take 200 wickets in Test cricket?
14. Who figured in England's tenth-wicket stand of 128 against the West Indies at The Oval in 1966?

15. Who was the last player to score 3,000 runs in an English season?

1	2	3	4	5	6	7	8	9	10	11	12	13	14	15
11	10	15	14	13	12	9	7	8	6	1	2	3	4	5

Answers: **1.** They were all stumpings **2.** 1937 (v New Zealand) **3.** Australia's Richie Benaud **4.** John Snow and Ken Higgs **5.** Bill Alley (Somerset) in 1961 **6.** 309 **7.** A full pitch ball aimed, intentionally or unintentionally, at the batsman's head **8.** Lance Gibbs (West Indies) **9.** Sydney Cricket Ground **10.** The sweep **11.** South Africa **12.** James Lillywhite **13.** World Series Cricket **14.** Andy Roberts **15.** An off-break delivered with leg-break action.

Go for the runs!

1. Was England bowler Jim Laker an off-spinner or leg-spinner?
2. Who was manager of Australia on her 1977 England tour?
3. From which wood is a cricket bat traditionally made?
4. At which ground would you find the Vauxhall end?
5. Who captained India against the West Indies in 1978/79?
6. What is the origin of the term 'a duck'?
7. From which West Indian island does Viv Richards come?
8. Whose world Test wickets record did Lance Gibbs break?
9. Who sponsors the English county championship?
10. In which series did England last regain the Ashes?

11. What is the record for most runs in a Test series and who set it?
12. What was unusual about England's home series in 1912?
13. What were Jim Laker's overall figures in the 1956 Manchester Test between England and Australia?
14. Which Australian made a century in his first Test batting at No. 7?

15. Who was the Oxford University freshman who scored a century on his Test debut at Manchester in 1959?

1	2	3	4	5	6	7	8	9	10	11	12	13	14	15
11	10	9	15	14	12	8	7	6	13	1	2	3	4	5

Answers: 1. 974 by Sir Don Bradman for Australia v England, 1930 2. It was a triangular tournament with Australia and South Africa 3. 19–90 4. Greg Chappell 5. A. A. Baig for India v England 6. Schweppes 7. Freddie Trueman 8. Antigua 9. Willow 10. Len Maddocks 11. Off spinner 12. A duck's egg i.e. 0 13. Australia's 1977 tour 14. Sunil Gavaskar 15. The Oval.

Go for the runs!

1. On which English tour did the 'bodyline' controversy arise?
2. In which year was the first Prudential World Cup?
3. When was the last time the English county championship tied?
4. In which country would you watch a Sheffield Shield match?
5. Who is South Africa's leading Test wicket-taker?
6. When was New Zealand's first Test victory over England?
7. Who was the defeated England captain in that match?
8. What aid did umpires first use in Pakistan's 1978 tour of England?
9. For what use were sheep kept at Lord's in the 18th century?
10. What do the initials WCA stand for?

11. What is the lowest Test score by Australia?
12. How did the term hat-trick originate?
13. Who won the 1976/77 Sheffield Shield?
14. Who was the only New Zealander to have played World Series Cricket by the end of 1978?

15. Which record did Sunil Gavaskar set in the 3rd Test between India and the West Indies at Calcutta in 1979?

1	2	3	4	5	6	7	8	9	10	11	12	13	14	15
12	11	10	15	14	13	1	2	3	4	5	6	7	8	9

Answers: **1.** Geoff Boycott **2.** Light meters **3.** Grass-cutting **4.** Women's Cricket Association **5.** 36 v England in 1902 **6.** A bowler was presented with a hat for taking three wickets in successive balls **7.** Western Australia **8.** Richard Hadlee **9.** He became the only player to score a century in each innings of a Test on three separate occasions **10.** 1977, between Middlesex and Kent **11.** 1975 **12.** The 1932/33 **13.** On England's 1977/78 tour, Christchurch **14.** Hugh Tayfield, 170 **15.** Australia.

36

1. In which remarkable Test victory did these two batsmen star in 1976?
2. Who are they and what was their contribution?
3. What was remarkable about the way the last Test ended and what was the Series result?

Puzzle BB

Who's this?

1. Born Dunedin, 1947.
2. Figured in his country's highest first wicket stand of 387 with T. W. Jarvis against West Indies in 1971/72.
3. Plays English county cricket for Worcestershire.

37

1. They were two of four England players to accomplish the same feat on the 1972/73 tour of India and Pakistan—who are they and what was it?
2. Who were the other two?
3. Who lost the job as Pakistan captain for England's visit and who took over?

38 Name the Test bowlers

1

2

3

Puzzle CC

1. How did Currie and Rice go together well in 1979?

2. How did Hampshire lead Yorkshire in 1979?

Puzzle DD

Which England player has two saintly connections with winter and why?

4

Go for the runs!

1. What is South Africa's emblem?
2. Who was the West Indies wicket-keeper on their 1978/79 tour of India?
3. Who was the first English player to hit a Test century on the 1978/79 tour of Australia?
4. What is the main competition in India?
5. After whom was the Lord's ground named?
6. Who succeeded Hanif Mohammad as Pakistan captain?
7. Is Inshan Ali and Indian, West Indian or Pakistan player?
8. Whose 307 Test wickets make him the second most successful bowler of all time?
9. In which Test team would you have found an Engineer and a Contractor?
10. What is the Christian name of the third of the Chappell brothers?

11. Which player was nicknamed Johnny Won't Hit Today?
12. Who were the Middlesex 'twins'?
13. Why were Test series in Australia increased from five to six from 1970/71?
14. In which one series were England captained respectively by Mike Smith, Colin Cowdrey and Brian Close?

15. Who was the last Australian to take a Test hat-trick?

1	2	3	4	5	6	7	8	9	10	11	12	13	14	15
8	9	10	5	4	3	11	15	14	13	12	1	2	6	7

Answers: **1.** Bill Edrich and Denis Compton **2.** To allow Perth to become a Test centre **3.** Saeed Ahmed **4.** Thomas Lord **5.** The Ranji Trophy **6.** The 1966 tour by the West Indies **7.** Lindsay Kline v South Africa, Cape Town, 1957/58 **8.** The Springbok **9.** David Murray **10.** David Gower (Perth) **11.** West Indian **12.** England captain J. W. H. T. Douglas, renowned in Australia for stonewalling **13.** Trevor **14.** In an Indian Test side of 1961/62— Nari Contractor and Farokh Engineer **15.** Freddie Trueman.

Go for the runs!

1. What is the general term used in England for byes, leg byes, no balls etc?
2. Which South African made the then slowest Test century in 545 minutes against Australia in 1958?
3. Which English county plays at Edgbaston?
4. What is the maximum length of a cricket bat—36, 38 or 40 inches?
5. What type of spin bowler was Australia's Arthur Mailey?
6. Who was the youngest player to capture 200 Test wickets?
7. Which Indian player was known as Vinoo?
8. Is Clive Lloyd a left- or right-hand bat?
9. Who dismissed Washbrook for 6 and 8 and Hutton for 13 in his first two Tests?
10. For which English county did Walter Hammond play?

11. Who scored the first Test match century?
12. Which three England players scored centuries in England's record-making Test total of 903–7 dec. v Australia at The Oval in 1938?
13. Which was Mike Brearley's first Test defeat as England captain?
14. For which Test side did the top scorer make 11?

15. How were England involved in a 'Greek tragedy' during the 1935 tour by South Africa?

1	2	3	4	5	6	7	8	9	10	11	12	13	14	15
7	8	9	12	11	10	15	14	13	6	5	4	1	2	3

Answers: **1.** 3rd v Australia, Melbourne, 1979 **2.** New Zealand, in the lowest Test score of 26 v England, 1955 **3.** They were beaten at home for the first time by South Africa with Greek leg-spin bowler Xenophon Balaskas bagging nine wickets in the decisive Lord's Test **4.** L. Hutton (364), M. Leyland (187) and J. Hardstaff (169*) **5.** Charles Bannerman for Australia v England, 1877 **6.** Gloucestershire **7.** Extras **8.** Jackie McGlew **9.** Warwickshire **10.** Graham McKenzie (Australia) at 27 **11.** Leg spin and googlies **12.** 38 inches **13.** Ray Lindwall (Australia) **14.** Left **15.** Mulvantrai Mankad.

39

1. In which Test matches would you have seen these scenes?
2. Who are examining the pitch in picture B and why?
3. What's the incident in picture C?

A

B

Puzzle EE

Who's this?

1. Test batsman and captain.

2. Scored a century and a double century in the same Test in his first series, against West Indies in 1971.

3. Led his country to a 1–0 win over the West Indies in 1979.

Puzzle FF

What are these players' forenames?

1. . . . . Toohey (Australia).

2. . . . . Emburey (England).

3. . . . . Gomes (West Indies).

4. . . . . Darling (Australia).

5. . . . . Dev (India).

Go for the runs!

1. Who was the last Test player to be knighted?
2. True or false: Arthur Milton scored a century on his Test debut for England in 1958.
3. Was Australia's Alan Davidson a left- or right-arm bowler?
4. Which is South Australia's chief ground?
5. What is the name of the English Sunday competition?
6. What is a wicket maiden?
7. Which West Indian is known as 'Supercat' for his feline fielding prowess?
8. Who has captained Australia most times—Simpson, Chappell or Benaud?
9. In which year was the M.C.C. formed—in 1777, 1787 and 1797?
10. Which Australian captain had the Christian names Warwick Windridge?

11. What was Australia's first innings total in the 1977 Centenary Test against England?
12. Who holds the record for most wickets in a Test rubber?
13. Who was the first player to score a century in each innings of a first class match against Australia in England?
14. Who has won South Africa's Currie Cup most times?

15. What is the origin of the term 'popping crease'?

1	2	3	4	5	6	7	8	9	10	11	12	13	14	15
11	12	13	14	15	1	2	3	4	5	10	9	8	7	6

Answers: **1.** An over in which the batsman scores no runs and the bowler takes one or more wickets **2.** Clive Lloyd **3.** Ian Chappell, 30 **4.** 1787 **5.** W. W. Armstrong **6.** Instead of a line across the front of the wickets, it was the practice until the early 18th century of having a hole big enough to take the base of the bat, or the ball. To score a run it was necessary for the arriving batsman to get his bat into the hole before the fielder could 'pop' the ball into it **7.** Transvaal **8.** Colin Cowdrey, for Kent in 1961 **9.** England's S. F. Barnes, 49 v South Africa in 1913/14 **10.** 138 **11.** Sir Gary Sobers, in 1975 **12** True (v New Zealand at Leeds) **13.** Left **14.** Adelaide **15.** The John Player League.

Go for the runs!

1. Which former England opener played soccer for Tottenham Hotspur?
2. For which country did Jeff Stollmeyer play?
3. Whose 252 Test wickets are bettered only by Freddie Trueman and Lance Gibbs?
4. What is a full toss?
5. Who played his only two Tests for England against the West Indies in 1976?
6. Which cricketer has the middle name Sewards?
7. Which Kent and England batsman became a well-known Test umpire?
8. Which Australian scored a century in the third Test against England at Melbourne in 1978/79?
9. Who succeeded Bradman as Australia's captain in 1949?
10. Which English county plays at Lord's?

11. Who captained Australia in the first Test against England in 1877?
12. Which English county turned down Sir Jack Hobbs as a player?
13. Which former England captain won an F.A. Cup runners'-up medal with Southampton in 1902?
14. Which former England captain was also an Olympic boxing champion?

15. In which Australian touring team would you have found, among others, Dick-a-Dick, Mosquito, Tiger, Red Cap, Jim Crow and King Cole?

1	2	3	4	5	6	7	8	9	10	11	12	13	14	15
10	11	2	14	7	9	13	3	12	4	15	5	8	1	6

Answers: **1.** J. W. H. T. Douglas **2.** Brian Statham **3.** Graham Wood **4.** Middlesex **5.** Essex **6.** In the first Australian team to come to England, in 1868—they were all aborigines **7.** Chris Balderstone **8.** C. B. Fry **9.** Freddie Trueman **10.** Bill Edrich **11.** West Indies **12.** Lindsay Hassett **13.** Arthur Fagg **14.** A ball which does not pitch from bowler to batsman **15.** D. W. Gregory.

1. One of seven players to score ten centuries in the same series—can you name him?
2. Which and when was the series?
3. Who were the other century-makers?
4. What was significant about the results of the second Test of the series?
5. Who won the rubber and by what margin?
6. Who is the wicket-keeper pictured here?
7. Who were the respective series captains?

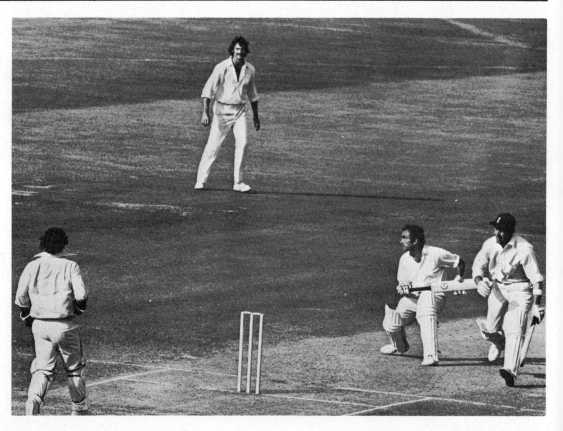

1. Who are the players in this mix-up?
2. In which Test series?
3. Which of the two scored a century in the series and where?
4. Who was the other player from the home side to score a century in the series?
5. Which two players scored Test centuries for the visitors?

Go for the runs!

1. What then record did Sir Don Bradman set in the Leeds Test between England and Australia in 1930?
2. Who was known as Plum?
3. Which English county plays at Old Trafford, Manchester?
4. Which country did Javed Burki captain?
5. Who is the youngest of Pakistan's Test-playing Mohammad brothers?
6. Who is the only overseas recognised batsman to have averaged 100 in an English season?
7. Launceston is the HQ of which Australian state side?
8. For which country does Norbert Phillip play?
9. What is the name of the famous room at Lord's?
10. What are the Christian names of New Zealand's Hadlee brothers?

11. Who was England's youngest Test captain?
12. Who leads the West Indies Test batting averages overall?
13. Which former England captain was once offered the Crown of Albania?
14. In which city would you find the Newlands Test ground?

15. In which Test did Australia's Chappell brothers first appear together?

1	2	3	4	5	6	7	8	9	10	11	12	13	14	15
12	11	15	14	13	8	7	5	4	1	3	10	9	6	2

Answers: **1.** Dayle and Richard **2.** At Perth, against England in 1970 **3.** M. P. Bowden, 23 v South Africa, 1889 **4.** The Long Room **5.** West Indies **6.** Cape Town, South Africa **7.** Tasmania **8.** Sir Don Bradman, 1938 **9.** C. B. Fry **10.** George Headley, 60.83 **11.** Former England captain Sir Pelham Warner **12.** The highest individual Test score of 334 **13.** Sadiq **14.** Pakistan **15.** Lancashire.

Go for the runs!

1. Who captained the 1978/79 England tourists in Australia?
2. What is a bye?
3. At which Test ground are Yorkshire's headquarters?
4. Which Kent opener was first picked for England in 1956?
5. Which cricketer has the Christian names Robert Baddeley?
6. What is the signal for a batsman given out?
7. Who was recalled as England opener against Australia in 1956 at the age of 41?
8. Who took the other wicket when Jim Laker took 19 wickets against Australia at Old Trafford in 1956?
9. Who succeeded Alan Knott as England wicket-keeper?
10. Which player was flown to Australia to bolster England's sagging fortunes in the 1974/75 tour?

11. Who was the first Pakistan player to score a century on his Test debut?
12. Which Australian Test ground is in Richmond Park?
13. What was the name of the club whose members formed the M.C.C.?
14. Who opened the batting for England in the Centenary Test against Australia in 1977?

15. Who was the first player to hit a century and a double century in the same Test?

1	2	3	4	5	6	7	8	9	10	11	12	13	14	15
7	6	13	12	2	1	11	10	5	4	15	14	9	8	3

Answers: **1.** The index finger raised **2.** Bobby Simpson **3.** Doug Walters, for Australia v West Indies, 1969, with 242 and 103 **4.** Colin Cowdrey **5.** Bob Taylor **6.** A run scored from a ball which is not touched by bat or batsman and which eludes the wicket-keeper **7.** Mike Brearley **8.** Bob Woolmer and Mike Brearley **9.** The White Conduit Club **10.** Tony Lock **11.** Cyril Washbrook **12.** Peter Richardson **13.** Headingley, Leeds **14.** Melbourne **15.** Billy Ibadulla, 166 v Australia at Karachi, 1964.

42

1. His record-equalling feat at Swansea during the West Indies' 1976 tour of England and Wales was one of cricket's most remarkable innings—who is he and what was it?
2. Who did he succeed as West Indies captain?
3. What is his highest Test score?

43

1. Why was it a case of forgive and forget with this English bowler after the last war?
2. How many Tests did he play in?
3. How many Test wickets did he take?
4. Who was his county and England partner?

Answers

1

1. Viv Richards (Somerset and West Indies) 2. 1976 v. England 3. Most runs (1,710) in a calendar year.

2

A. 1. Geoff Boycott (England) and Rohan Kanhai (West Indies) 2. Arthur Fagg 3. For a catch at the wicket; not out 4. Fagg threatened to withdraw after criticism by Kanhai, who later apologised B. 1. Mike Denness (England) 2. Australia 3. First Test, Edgbaston, 1975 C. 1. Australia and England (1958) 2. Left to Right: Gordon Rorke (Australia), Peter May and Wally Grout.

3

1. At The Oval, 1968 England v. Australia 2. England's Colin Cowdrey 3. Australia were 85–5 on the final day needing 352 to win 4. The crowd helped mop up the wicket 5. England won with six minutes to spare 6. Derek Underwood with 7–50 7. England squared the series at 1–1 but Australia retained the Ashes.

4

1. Sir Len Hutton 2. The highest Test score, 364, v. Australia, beaten by Sir Gary Sobers, 365 not out for West Indies v. Pakistan, 1957/58 3. Nought v. New Zealand, 1937.

5

1. Peter May (Surrey and England) 2. 285 not out v. West Indies, Edgbaston, 1957 3. A record 41 Tests as skipper 4. Peter Barker Howard.

6

John Reid, who captained New Zealand to her first Test win – over the West Indies.

7

Pakistan's Javed Miandad scored a century on his Test debut, against New Zealand, then at 19, became the youngest player to score a double century in a Test with 206 in the same series 2. New Zealand's P. J. Petherick took a hat-trick – the last Test player to do so 3. Pakistan won 2–0.

8

1. Neil Harvey 2. 6,149 3. Against England in 1961 at Lord's.

9

1. Alan Knott (England) bags his 220th Test victim, breaking Godfrey Evans's record for most Test dismissals, against the West Indies in the fifth Test at the Oval, 1976 2. Lawrence Rowe.

10

1. A: Clyde Walcott B: Everton Weekes C: Frank Worrell 2. The Three W's 3. Weekes 4. As a wicket-keeper 5. Weekes 6. Weekes and Walcott, 15 each 7. Worrell 8. Worrell and Walcott – and undefeated 574 for Barbados in 1945/46 9. Five double centuries in a season 10. Scoring a century in each innings of a Test match twice (Walcott did it in the same series).

11

1. Fred Titmus (A) and Frank Tyson (B) of England 2. England 3–1 3. Australia 3–1 4. Lawry (106) and Simpson (311) for Australia and Dexter (174) and Barrington (256) 5. Peter Burge and Jim Parks.

12

1. Keith Ross Miller 2. Victoria and New South Wales 3. Seven 4. 170 5. 281 for the Australians v. Leicestershire, Leicester, 1956 6. Aviators Keith and Ross Smith, who were the first to fly from England to Australia.

13

1. Wellington, New Zealand 2. Melbourne, Australia 3. Adelaide, Australia 4. Headingley (Leeds), England.

14

Glenn Turner (Worcestershire and New Zealand) – 1,000 runs by the end of May.

15

1. Ted Dexter 2. 1961/62 tour of India and Pakistan 3. Nine 4. 205, v. Pakistan, Karachi, 1961/62.

16

1. Roy Fredericks (West Indies) 2. David Steele (England) 3. Seymour Nurse (West Indies) 4. Peter Toohey (Australia).

17

1. Sir Jack Hobbs (left) and Herbert Sutcliffe of England 2. Eddie Barlow (left) and Graeme Pollock of South Africa 3. Bill Edrich (left) and Denis Compton of England.

18

1. Wasim Bari (Pakistan) 2. Ken Wadsworth (New Zealand) 3. Bob Taylor (England) 4. Rodney Marsh (Australia).

19

1. Richie Benaud (Australia) 2. He was the first player to take 200 wickets and score 2,000 runs in Tests 3. True.

20

1. Australia's Alan Davidson 2. A last-wicket stand of 98 with Graham McKenzie 3. Australia were able to set England 256 to win, bowled them out with 54 runs to spare and took a 2–1 lead to make sure of retaining the Ashes.

21

1 and 6 – Jim Laker and Tony Lock (England) 2 and 5 – Wes Hall and Charlie Griffith (West Indies) 3 and 4 – Andy Roberts and Michael Holding (West Indies).

22

1. Deep fine leg 2. Third man 3. Long leg 4. First slip 5. Second slip 6. Third slip 7. Gully 8. Short slip 9. Point 10. Short fine leg (or leg slip) 11. Short leg 12. Square leg 13. Cover point 14. Silly mid off 15. Short extra cover 16. Silly mid on (or forward short leg) 17. Midwicket 18. Mid off 19. Mid on 20. Deep extra cover 21. Long off 22. Long on.

23

1. David Gower (England) 2. Barry Richards (South Africa) 3. Sir Gary Sobers (West Indies).

24

1 and 5 – Greg and Ian Chappell (Australia) 2 and 6 – Graeme and Peter Pollock (South Africa) 3 and 4 – Sadiq and Mushtaq Mohammad (Pakistan).

25

1. The 1977 India v. England series 2. Gundappa Viswanath, caught Brearley bowled Underwood 3. Viswanath was out in the third and fourth Tests, caught Brearley bowled Underwood 4. England, 3–1.

26

1. England's Derek Randall, in the 1977 Centenary Test between Australia and England at Melbourne 2. 174 in England's second innings 3. Out caught Marsh bowled Lillee in the first innings 4. In the fourth Test between Australia and England at Sydney, 1979.

27

1. Eddie Barlow (South Africa) 2. Zaheer Abbas (Pakistan) 3. Rick McCosker (Australia).

28

1. Colin Cowdrey 2. Mike Denness 3. Tony

Lewis 4. Tony Greig 5. Ted Dexter 2. None 3. Ted Dexter 4. Colin Cowdrey 5. Tony Greig (South Africa), Tony Lewis (Wales), Mike Denness (Scotland) 6. Mike Denness (1974/75) 7. Tony Lewis 8. Tony Greig.

29

1 and 4 – Freddie Trueman and Brian Statham (England) 2 and 5 – Ray Lindwall and Keith Miller (Australia) 3 and 6 – Jeff Thomson and Dennis Lillee (Australia).

30

1. Lance Gibbs (West Indies) 2. Graham McKenzie (Australia) 3. John Snow (England) 4. Ian Botham (England).

31

1. He's Derek Underwood and at 17 he became the youngest bowler to take 100 wickets in a season 2. 77 (incl. three for Rest of World) 3. 219 4. 8–51 v. Pakistan, Lord's, 1974 5. He joined Kerry Packer's World Series Cricket.

32

1. Mike Brearley (England) 2. Bobby Simpson (Australia) 3. Alvin Kallicharran West Indies) 4. Bill Lawry (Australia).

33

1. England Test bowler Bob Willis is such a big fan of singer Bob Dylan (inset) that he took the name Dylan as the last of his Christian names – Robert George Dylan 2. The father of English television newscaster Reginald Bosanquet (inset) was B. J. T. Bosanquet, who is credited with inventing the googly, or bosie, as it's called in Australia.

34

1. Sir Jack Hobbs 2. The Master 3. With Wilfred Rhodes he figured in England's highest opening stand (323) against Australia, in 1911/12; and with Herbert Sutcliffe in 1926 he set England on the way to regaining the Ashes for the first time since before the war with a second innings opening stand of 172 on a treacherous Oval wicket, both players scoring centuries 4. He beat W. G. Grace's 126 and went on to 197 5. Denis Compton (18), 1947 6. 1963.

35

1. Australia's Bob Massie, who took 16 for 137 against England – bettered only by Jim Laker (19 for 90 for England v. Australia, 1956) and Sydney Barnes (17 for 159 for England v. South Africa, 1913/14) 2. 2–2.

36

1. They were members of the Indian side which scored a match-winning 406–4 in their fourth innings – the largest winning total for a Test side batting fourth – in the third Test against the West Indies 2. Sunil Gavaskar (left) and Gundappa Viswanath each scored centuries 3. Indian captain Bishen Bedi declared their second innings at 97–5 when only 12 runs ahead saying five players were unfit to bat. The West Indies won by ten wickets to take the series 2–1.

37

1. Tony Greig (left) and Dennis Amiss, who both score their maiden Test centuries 2. Tony Lewis and Keith Fletcher 3. Intikhab Alam was replaced as skipper by Majid Khan.

38

1. Ray Illingworth (England) 2. Intikhab Alam (Pakistan) 3. B. S. Chandrasekhar (India) 4. Len Pascoe (Australia).

39

1. A: Second Test at Lord's between England and Australia, 1975 B: Third Test at Headingley between England and Australia, 1975 C: Third Test at Lord's between England and West Indies in 1973 2. England captain Tony Greig (left) and Australia's Ian Chappell after vandals had dug it up, causing the match to be abandoned 3. A bomb scare.

40

1. England's Godfrey Evans 2. The 1950 England v. West Indies series 3. Len Hutton (202*) and Cyril Washbrook (114 and 102) for England; Alan Rae (106 and 109), Clyde Walcott (168), Everton Weekes (129) and Frank Worrell (261 and 138) for West Indies 4. West Indies won their first Test in England 5. West Indies 3–1 6. Clyde Walcott 7. Norman Yardley (England) and John Goddard.

41

1. John Edrich (left) and David Steele of England 2. The 1975 England v. Australia series 3. Edrich, at Lord's 4. Bob Woolmer (The Oval) 5. Ian Chappell and Rick McCosker (The Oval).

42

1. Clive Lloyd – 201* in 120 minutes against Glamorgan equalled Gilbert Jessop's record for the fastest double century 2. Rohan Kanhai 3. 242 not out against India, Bombay, 1974/75.

43

1. He's Harold Larwood, who was involved in the famous bodyline controversy of England's 1932/33 tour of Australia, but who settled in Australia and became an Australian citizen after the last war 2. 21 3. 78 4. Bill Voce.

The left hand page

A. 1. Sir Gary Sobers (West Indies) 8,032, excluding Rest of World matches 2. R. N. Harvey (Australia) 6,149 3. W. M. Lawry (Australia) 5,234 4. J. H. Edrich (England) 5,138 excl. RoW matches B. 1. Edrich, P. Richardson (2,061) 2. G. Pullar (1,974) 3. P. Parfitt (1,882) C. Sobers D. Derek Underwood (England) 265, excl. RoW matches E. Glenn Turner – all the others are left-handers F. Max Walker – all the others are left-armers G. Chris Old

Find the player

1. Barry Richards 2. Clive Lloyd 3. Dennis Lillee 4. Dennis Amiss 5. Zaheer Abbas 6. Bishen Bedi.

Puzzle Answers

A

1. Engineer 2. Parks and Marsh 3. Taylor 4. Knott

B

1. Close 2. May 3. Boycott 4. Smith

C

Arthur Milton (Gloucestershire and Arsenal) six Test caps and one soccer cap (v. Austria, 1951) and **Willie Watson** (Yorkshire, Leicestershire and Sunderland) 23 Test caps and two soccer caps (v. Ireland, 1950 and Wales, 1951).

D

They are the only English batsmen to have carried their bats through a completed Test innings – Hutton doing it twice.

E

1. Old Trafford 2. Lord's 3. The Oval

F

Zaheer Abbas (Pakistan)

G

1. Gundappa 2. Craig 3. Haroon 4. Ali 5. Joel 6. Mike

H

Ian Chappell (Australia)

J

Mushtaq Mohammad (Pakistan)

K

Colin Cowdrey (England)

L

1. S. C. Griffith (140 v. West Indies, Port of Spain, 1948) 2. P. B. H. May (138 v. South Africa, Leeds, 1951) 3. C. A. Milton (104* v. New Zealand, Leeds, 1958) 4. J. H. Hampshire (107 v. West Indies, Lord's, 1969) 5. F. C. Hayes (106* v. West Indies, Oval, 1963).

M

Rohan Kanhai (West Indies)

N

1. Valentine and May 2. Miller and Lillee

P

1. Lawrence Rowe (214 and 100* for the West Indies v. New Zealand at Kingston, 1972) 2. W. R. Endean (South Africa v. England, Capetown, 1956/57) 3. Geoff Griffin (South Africa v. England, Lord's, 1960).

Q

1. W. G. Grace (England) 2. Pahlan Umrigar (India) 3. W. J. O'Reilly (Australia) or E. J. Smith (England) 4. Sir Jack Hobbs (England) 5. Trevor Bailey (England) 6. Sunil Gavaskar (India) 7. The Nawab of Pataudi (India) 8. Ted Dexter (England) 9. Basil D'Oliveira (England) 10. Jeff Thomson (Australia) 11. N. B. F. Mann (South Africa) 12. Colin Cowdrey (England) 13. Sir Don Bradman (Australia) 14. A. P. Freeman (England) 15. Freddie Trueman (England) 16. A. L. Thomson (Australia).

R

Captain Cook!

S

Dennis Lillee (Australia)

T

Freddie Trueman (England)

U

1. Robert Abel (England) 2. W. W. Armstrong (Australia) 3. C. G. McCartney (Australia) 4. Kumar Shri Duleepsinhji (England) 5. Alan Davidson (Australia) 6. Ray Lindwall (Australia) 7. Ian Botham (England) 8. Joel Garner (West Indies)

V

Dennis Lillee (Australia)

W

Viv Richards (West Indies)

X

Tony Lock (England)

Y

1. J. and J. Hardstaff 2. L. and R. A. Hutton 3. F. G. and F. T. Mann 4. J. H. and J. M. Parks 5. F. W. and M. W. Tate 6. C. L. and D. C. H. Townsend.

Z

Ray Lindwall (Australia)

AA

1. Geoff Boycott of the Yorkshire committee who sacked him as captain 2. Wisden on bodyline bowling 3. Tony Greig on the 1976 tour by the West Indies 4. John Arlott commentating when Tufty Mann bowled George Mann in the 1948/49 Test series between South Africa and England.

BB

Glenn Turner (New Zealand)

CC

1. Clive Rice (Notts.) helped Transvaal to win the 1979 Currie Cup in South Africa. 2. John Hampshire was appointed Yorkshire captain for the 1979 season.

DD

John Augustine Snow.

EE

Sunil Gavaskar (India)

FF

1. Peter 2. John 3. Larry 4. Rick 5. Kapil